What Little Brown Girls Can Be!

By

Mista B. Belly

This book belongs to...

____

Once upon a time in a world not so far away

There lived a little brown girl with beautiful
natural kinky hair
At night she would look out her window and stare

She had a dream, you see, and she knew just what to do

She'd work harder than everyone and make it true,

She wanted to be a fire fighter,

strong and brave

She wanted to be a hair dresser,

with style and grace

She wanted to be a veterinarian,

with a kind and gentle touch

She wanted to be an army soldier,

fighting for what's just

She wanted to be a baker,

with a delicious treat

She wanted to be a judge,

with wisdom and seat

She wanted to be a pilot,

soaring through the sky

She wanted to be a scholar,

with a curious mind and eye

She wanted to be a gamer,

with quick reflexes and skill

She wanted to be a police officer,

protecting with a thrill

She wanted to be an astronaut,

reaching for the stars

She wanted to be a lawyer,

with a voice that never mars

She wanted to be an engineer,
with a clever mind and hand

She'd be anything she
wanted, if she put her heart
and mind to it, she'd stand

So the little brown girl grew and grew
And she worked hard, with all that she knew
And before she knew it, she was all grown up
And she became everything she wanted, with hard work no luck

So remember, little ones, that you can be anything you desire
With hard work, determination, and a spark that never tires
So chase your dreams and make them true
Just like the little brown girl, and see what you can do.

Made in the USA
Coppell, TX
17 April 2023